He went down, down, down.
But he fell into the river
and he could not get out.

'Help! Help!' called the ant.
'What can I do?'

A dove saw the ant in the river.

'I will help you,' she said.

'I have got a leaf.'

The dove put the leaf in the river.
'Get on the leaf,' she said.

The ant got on the leaf.
It was like a little boat.

The ant said to the dove,
'One day I will help you.'
The dove said to the ant,
'You are too little to help.'

One day a man saw the dove.
The man had a bow and arrow.
'I will get you,' said the man.

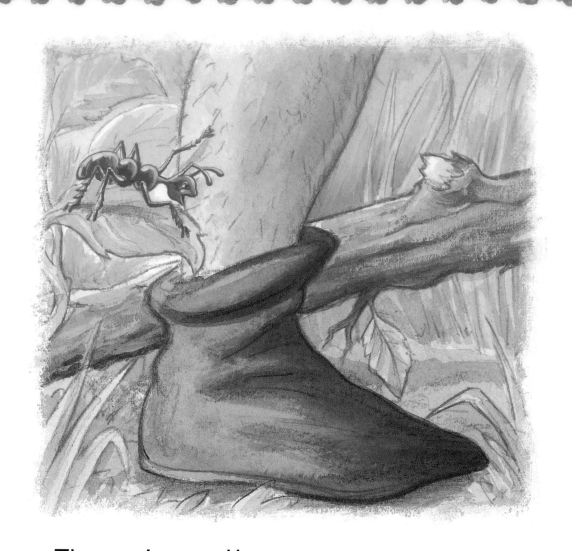

The ant saw the man.

'Now I can help the dove,' he said.

'I can stop the man.'

The ant did stop the man.

'Ow! Ow! Ow!' said the man.
The man jumped up and down
and the arrow went into the river.

'I did help you,' said the ant.

'Yes, you did,' said the dove.